DINOSAUR

Drawing, Doodling,
and Coloring Book

ARCTURUS

ARCTURUS

This edition published in 2016 by Arcturus Publishing Limited
26/27 Bickels Yard, 151–153 Bermondsey Street,
London SE1 3HA

Design: Paul Oakley
Text: Frances Evans
Illustrations: Steve Beaumont: pages 16-17, 30-31, 32-33, 40, 48-49, 58-59,
64-65, 76, 80-81, 92-93. Beccy Blake: pages 8, 21, 27, 34-35, 36, 45, 53,
60, 62, 66-67, 72, 91, 94. The Bright Agency/Tom Knight/Michael Garton:
pages 4, 6-7, 25, 38-39, 46, 50-51, 68, 69, 73, 74-75, 82-83, 88, 91, 96.
Kate Daubney: pages 5, 10-11, 14-15, 20, 41, 42-43, 70-71, 95. Flameboy:
pages 9, 40, 92-93. Louise Forshaw: pages 3, 12, 18-19, 28, 44, 47, 54-55,
61, 77, 78-79, 91.
Front cover artwork by Louise Forshaw
Back cover artwork by Beccy Blake

ISBN: 978-1-78599-264-3
CH004991US
Supplier 26, Date 0516, Print run 5330

Printed in China

Color in the Stegosauruses and draw the rest of their family.

Draw a friend for this Iguanodon.

Fill the sky with as many pterosaurs as you can.

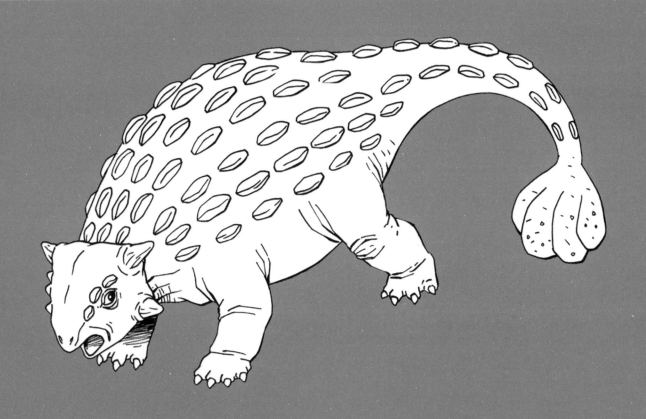

Pick some colors for these
tough armored dinos!

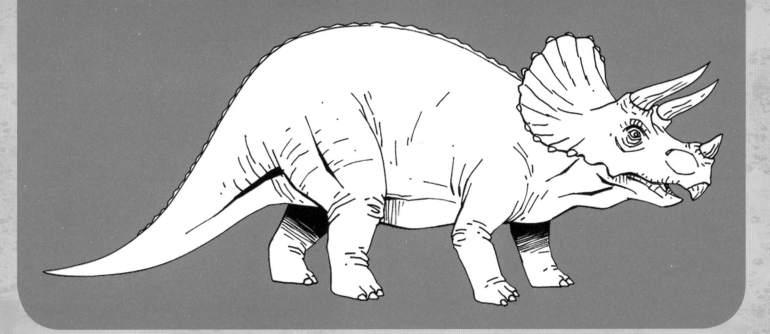

Hang some pictures of your favorite dinosaurs on the wall!

What's this Ankylosaurus about to battle?

You're on a trek in the Jurassic jungle!
Color in your camping gear.

Doodle what you've discovered on a dino dig...

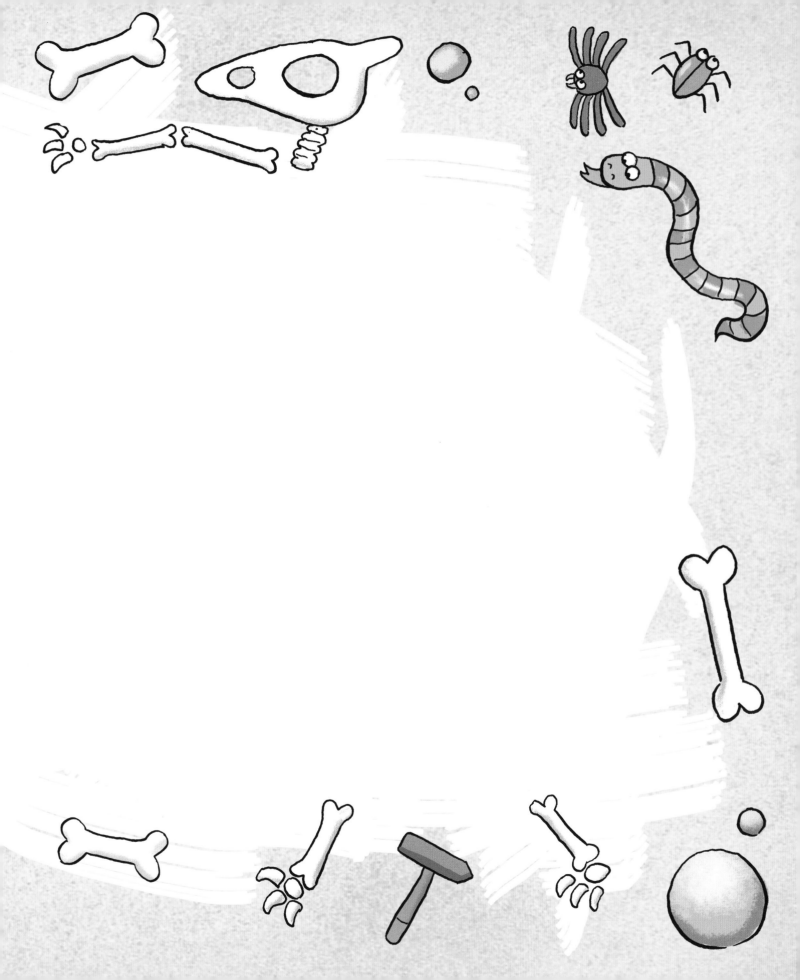

How to Draw... T. rex

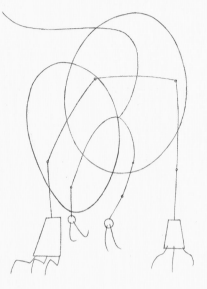

Step 1

Draw the basic stick figure.

Step 2

Add construction shapes around the legs and arms. Draw the outline of the jaws and tail. Remove your stick-figure lines.

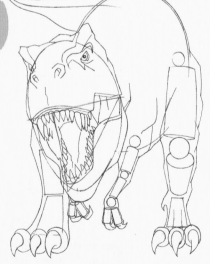

Step 3

Now draw skin around the construction shapes and add the face and teeth.

Step 4

Remove the construction shapes Add some scales to the skin.

Have a go at drawing your own T. rex!

Now doodle the fearsome T. rex that's chasing this group of Triceratops...

What do you think a dinosaur would dream about?

Color the giant dragonflies first,
then finish the picture!

Color all the plant-eaters...

... then color in the carnivores!

Yikes! What wild beast
have you bumped into?

This Spinosaurus looks pretty scary.
Draw an even fiercer one underneath!

Draw a sauropod with an even
longer neck than this one!

These baby dinos are hatching! Draw their proud parents.

Use as many shades of green as you can on these jungle leaves!

Color in these monsters of the deep...

How to Draw... Triceratops

Step 1

Start with the basic stick figure.

Step 2

Add some construction shapes.

Step 3

Now draw the frill, face, and mouth. Add skin around the construction shapes, too.

Step 4
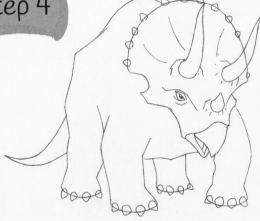

Remove all the stick lines and shapes. Add the horns and toes to finish it off.

Draw your own tough Triceratops here!

Now fill this page with as many Triceratops as you can!

What do you think has
made these tracks?

Color each Diplodocus, Triceratops, and Stegosaurus a different shade.

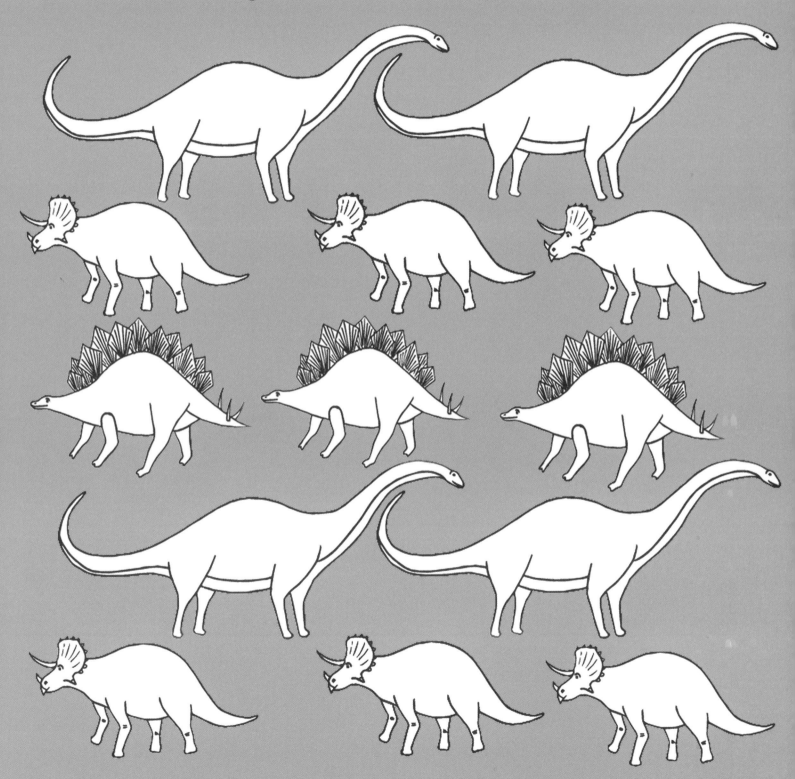

Utahraptors could run really fast!
Draw what this one is chasing.

Make this safari outfit camouflaged!

Color in these friendly dinosaurs.

Draw the dinosaur you've spotted through your binoculars.

Make this volcano erupt!

And doodle some
dinos running away.

How to Draw... Velociraptor

Step 1

Start with the basic stick figure.

Step 2

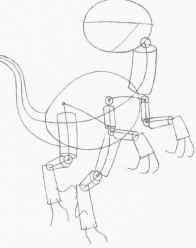

Add some construction shapes and draw the tail. Then draw the outline of the jaw.

Step 3

Draw the face and claws and add skin around the construction shapes. Remove the stick-figure lines.

Step 4

Remove the construction shapes. Add the teeth and some skin creases.

Now draw a fearsome Velociraptor!

Velociraptors hunted in packs. Doodle as many as you can on this page...

Design a backpack to take on your dino trek!

Use some of these bones to doodle a dinosaur skeleton.

Finish off this dinosaur scene!

Color in these giant prehistoric dragonflies!

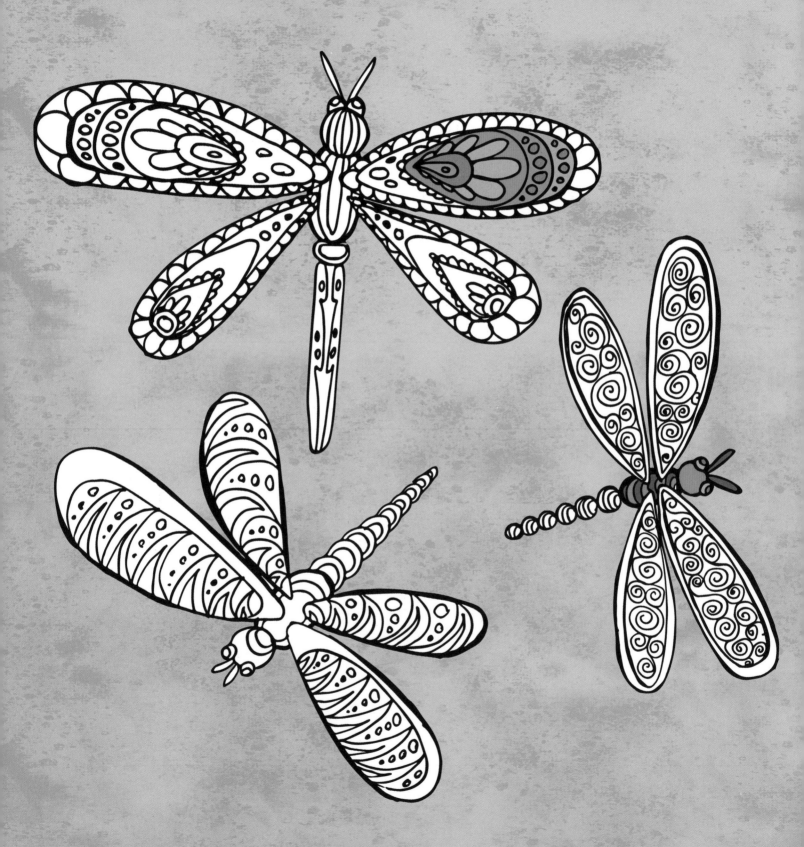

What would a T. rex and a Stegosaurus look like if they got mixed up?

What dinosaur would you like to see at the museum?

Doodle a tasty forest for this Brachiosaurus to munch on.

This dinosaur needs protection!
Draw him some armor.

Color in this funky dino egg!

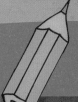
How to Draw... Diplodocus

Step 1

Start by drawing the basic stick figure.

Step 2

Add construction shapes to build up the body.

Step 3

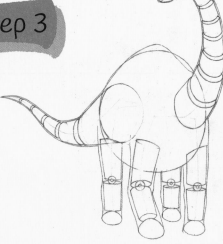

Add the skin by drawing around the shapes. Start to remove your stick-figure lines. Then draw the face.

Step 4

Remove your construction shapes. Add details such as claws, wrinkles, and leaves for it to munch on.

Now you give it a go!

their heads above the trees!

Draw your favorite carnivore.

Doodle a dino with a brilliant crest, just like this Parasaurolophus!

Color in these snoozing dinos...

Make these Pterodactyls
stand out in the sky!

Fill this page with lots of prehistoric sea creatures!

Choose bright colors for this Archaeopteryx's feathers!

If you were a dinosaur, what would you eat for dinner?

This Pterodactyl is flying over a huge herd of dinosaurs—draw them here!

How to Draw... Stegosaurus

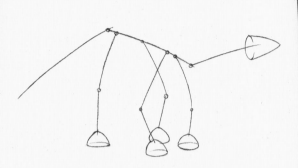

Start with the basic stick figure lines.

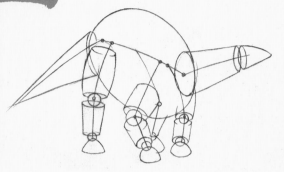

Then add the construction shapes.

Add the skin by drawing around the construction shapes. Draw the plates, claws, and mouth. Remove your stick lines.

Remove your construction shapes. Add detail to the face, skin, and plates.

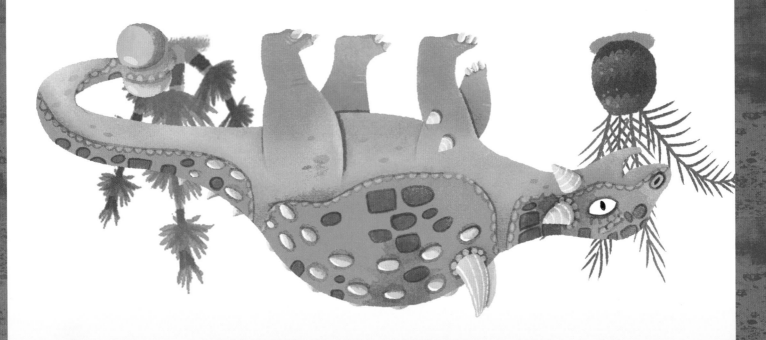

Draw another Ankylosaurus
with a really strong club!

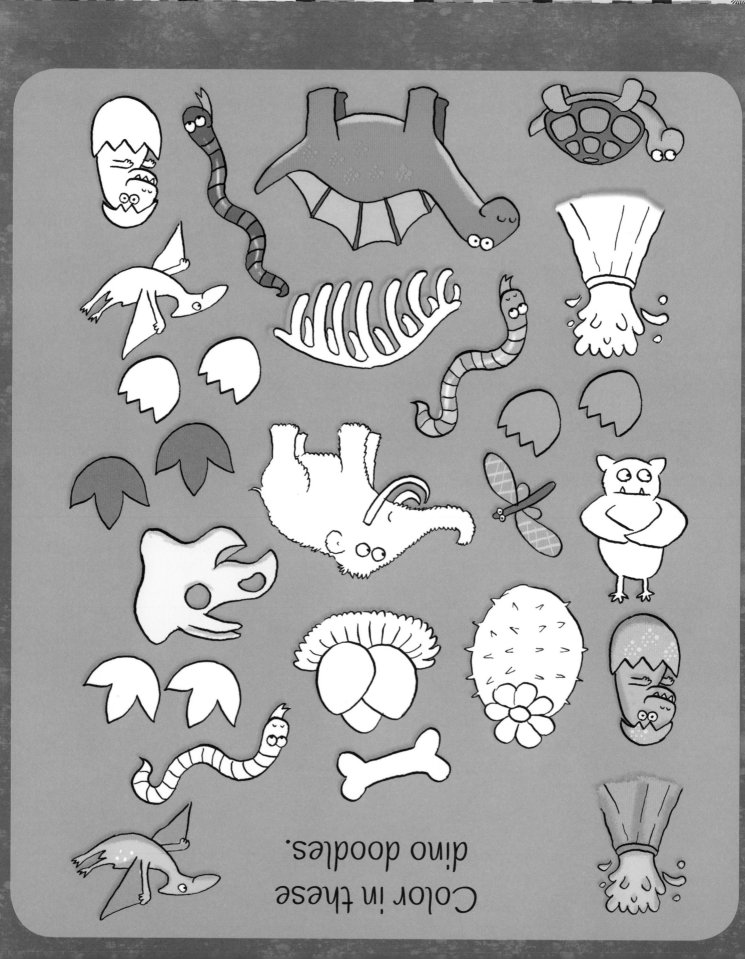

Color in these
dino doodles.

Draw something cute
in this dinosaur nest!

Color in these fierce carnivores.

What's your favorite herbivore?
Draw a gentle giant here!

Doodle a cave for this fearsome
Dimetrodon to live in.

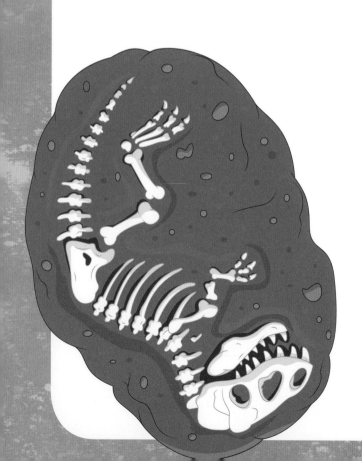

Draw this dinosaur
when it was alive!

What would a Diplodocus and a
Pterodactyl look like if they got mixed up?

Make each dinosaur really colorful!

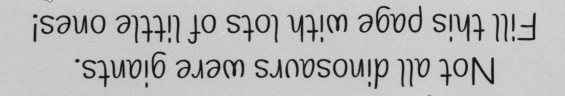

Not all dinosaurs were giants.
Fill this page with lots of little ones!

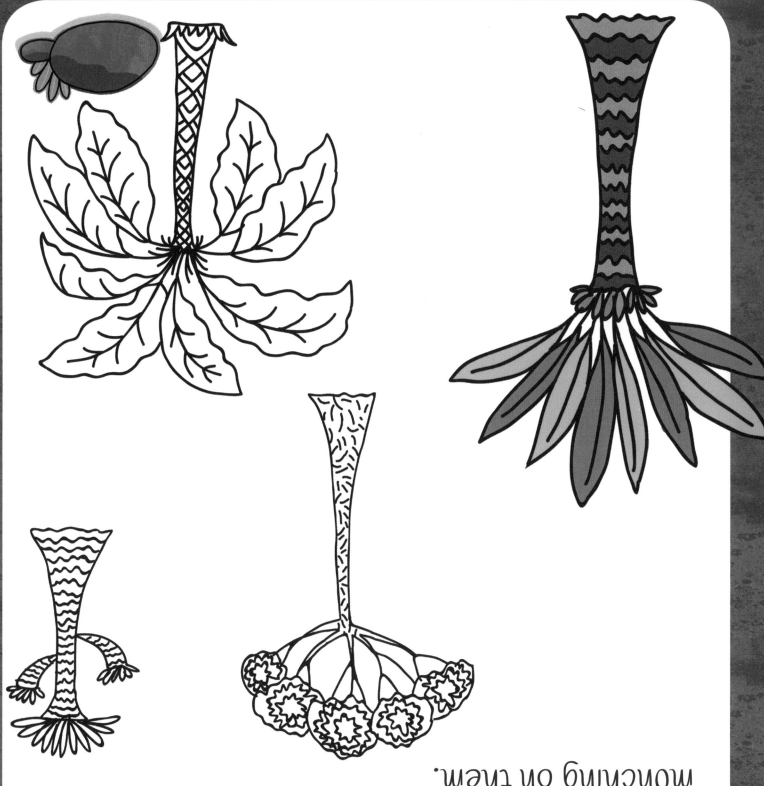

Color in these trees and draw some dinos munching on them.

Draw some dino friends for this
colorful Stegosaurus.

Try drawing your own Stegosaurus here!